What are Materials?

What do you think of when you think of materials?

1   Write a definition for what a material is, so that a younger child could understand.

_____

_____

2   Draw a picture of the inside of a house.

2a Include lots of different furniture in your picture. A lot of different materials are used to build a house and make the furniture and household items inside it.

2b Label the materials of the furniture and household items.

2c In your picture, identify items made from materials with the following properties: hard, soft, rigid, flexible, shiny, dull, transparent, opaque.

3   Why is a guinea pig cage not suitable for pets to live outside in a cold country?

_____

_____

Properties of Materials

1 Look at the properties listed below. Describe each of these properties to a younger child.

Hard _____

Absorbent _____

Soluble _____

Transparent _____

Electrical conductor _____

Thermal insulator _____

Magnetic _____

2 Record three properties of the materials for each of these toys.

1	1	1
2	2	2
3	3	3

Exploring the Properties of Materials

1 Record two ways you have classified the materials. Show clearly how you have sorted them into groups.

_____

_____

_____

_____

_____

_____

_____

_____

2 Record a *Which material?* riddle. Ask your classmate to guess the material.

_____

_____

_____

_____

Materials Around School

1   Draw two different types of classrooms. Label the materials in each classroom.

2   Which materials are used in one room that are not used in the other?

_____

_____

3   Materials in the classroom. Look at the diagram in the topic book, then use the table below to record the properties of each item. Place a tick in a box if you think the object has the material property listed. Use a cross if it does not.

	Soft	Flexible	Strong	Predict! Is it attracted to a magnet?	Test! Is it attracted to a magnet?
ruler					
protractor					
eraser					
paperclip					
pencil case					
paper					
sticky-tac					
pencil					
compasses					
tissue					
mouse mat					
rubber band					

More Than One Material

1 Which materials do you think this modern table could be made out of?

2 Why are the materials you suggest good choices?

3 Choose four things from around your home or school that are made
   from more than one material. List the materials they are made from
   and record why you think these materials are used.

Household item	Materials used	Reasons materials used

Electrical Conductivity

1   **Complete the sentences.**

A material is an electrical conductor if _____

_____

A material is an electrical insulator if _____

_____

2   **Draw and label a picture of the inside of an electrical plug.**

The pins are made out of metal because

_____

_____

The case is made out of plastic because

_____

_____

Ia Draw what you think is inside a cosmic ball.
Ib Label the parts.

2   Complete the Venn diagram. Use objects and materials found in
    your bedroom.

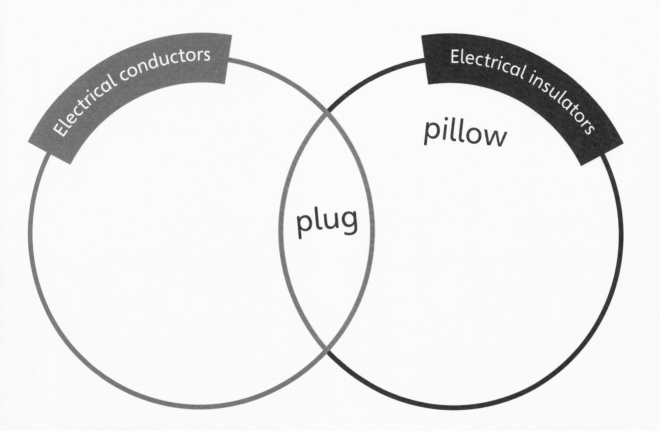

Electrical conductors

Electrical insulators

pillow

plug

Thermal Insulation

1 Complete the sentences.

A good thermal conductor is _____

A good thermal insulator is _____

2 What materials are these toys made from? Add labels to the diagram.
3 The toys have been in the hot sun for several hours. Which toys will be too hot to pick up and put back in the toy box? Why?

_____

_____

4 Which toys will be cool enough to pick up? Why?

_____

_____

Insulating Gloves

1   Record the results of your investigation into insulating gloves. Use this table and graph.

Type of glove	Time to feel heat from the spoon

2   Draw a graph showing how long it took for the heat of the spoon to be felt wearing gloves made from different materials.

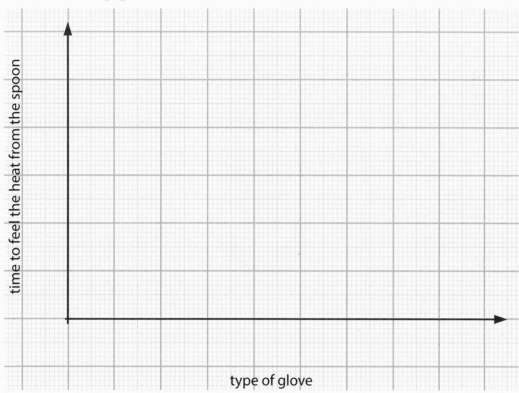

time to feel the heat from the spoon

type of glove

3   The best gloves to wear to put the toys away are

_____

Because _____

_____

Keeping our Food and Drink Warm

1a Which is the best container to keep food hot?

_____

1b Explain your choice.

_____

_____

2a Label the parts of the vacuum flask. Label the materials used.

2b Explain why these materials have been chosen.

_____

_____

3   Do you think this flask could be used to keep something cold?
    Explain your thinking.

_____

_____

Science Skills

How Well a Flask Keeps Water Hot – Investigate it!

1   Complete the table with your measurements.

Time lapsed	Temperature	Time lapsed	Temperature
start		2.5 hours	
0.5 hours		3 hours	
I hour		3.5 hours	
I.5 hours		4 hours	
2 hours			

2   Now draw a graph of the results.

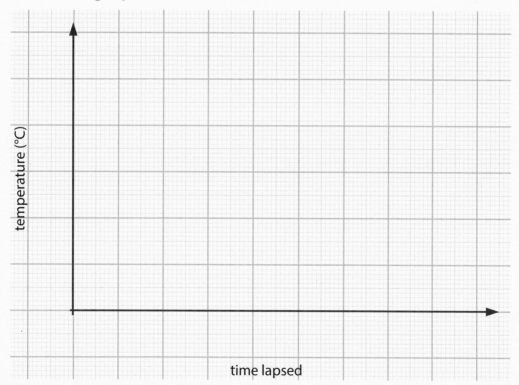

3   Explain these results.

Investigating Materials

1   Which materials do you think should be avoided when building an environmentally friendly building?

To help save the planet I would avoid using _____

Because _____

_____

Making a chair.

2   Look at the picture. What is this test trying to find out?

_____

3   Which materials could you use to stuff a sofa?

_____

4   How could you find out which was best?

_____

5   Which materials could you use to cover the sofa?

_____

6   How would you decide which is best?

_____

Science Skills

Which Material? Investigate it!

Questions about materials to investigate.

Ia Record your choice of four questions about the best materials for different everyday objects.

Ib Predict which you think is the best material, and explain why you have chosen it.

Question I _____

I think that _____

Because _____

Question 2 _____

I think that _____

Because _____

Question 3 _____

I think that _____

Because _____

Question 4 _____

I think that _____

Because _____

Candy Laces - Test it!

I   We need to be clear with our instructions on how to carry out the investigation. Explain why each step is important.

Describe clearly what they will do

_____

_____

List equipment they will use

_____

_____

List the things they will keep the same to make it a fair test

_____

_____

Plan to do each test more than once and take an average

_____

_____

Prepare a table to show how they will record their results

_____

Describe the type of graph or chart they will be using

_____

Jay's Investigation

This is the table of results from the investigation Jay carried out.

1 **Calculate the average stretch of each lace and then draw a graph of the results.**

Type of lace	Amount of stretch	Average stretch
Strawberry	A 5 cm B 6 cm C 7 cm	
Liquorice	A 3 cm B 3 cm C 3 cm	
Sugar-coated cola	A 4 cm B 3 cm C 3.5 cm	

2 **Which lace stretches the most?**

My Stretchy Lace Investigation

1 Plan your own stretchy lace investigation, and record what you would do. Number the steps in your instructions. You can draw pictures to help.

This is how I would carry out an investigation to find out the stretchiest type of candy lace ...

Table of results:

Graph of results:

We found out that ...

_____

We think this is because ...

_____

_____

Which Tape is Stickiest When Wet?

Method

To find out which tape retains its stickiness best when wet we will …

_____

_____

_____

_____

_____

_____

_____

_____

_____

We will need the following equipment …

_____

_____

_____

_____

_____

The results below show …

My conclusion is …

_____

_____

_____

_____

Surviving in the Desert

1   In this table make a list of things you would pack for a desert trip.
    Record the material each thing is made from and why it is needed.

Item needed	Material	Why it is needed

2   Draw a diagram of an enclosure for a turtle or a giraffe. Label the
    different features and the materials they are made from.

My _____ enclosure

Materials for a Guinea Pig Cage

Material	Is the material a sensible choice? (Write Yes or No.)	Why is the material a sensible choice or not a sensible choice?
wood		
cardboard		
paper		
metal		
polythene		
glass		
plastic		
fleece		
straw		
rock		
bubble wrap		
tissue		
cotton		

Properties of Materials

Check your knowledge and understanding.

1   **Choose a material that matches each of these pairs of descriptions of properties.**

Transparent and brittle _____

Shiny and conducts electricity _____

Flexible and elastic _____

Soft and a good thermal insulator _____

Transparent and flexible _____

Dull and an electrical insulator _____

Hard and attracted to a magnet _____

Weak and absorbent _____

Weak and waterproof _____

An electrical and thermal insulator _____